A Year
In the M

A Book of Days

Illustrated by Benjamin Perkins

Bloomsbury Books
London

First published in 1990
© 1990 Savitri Books (this edition and this design)
© 1990 Benjamin Perkins (all illustrations)
This edition published 1992 by Bloomsbury Books
an imprint of The Godfrey Cave Group
42 Bloomsbury Street, London WC1B 3QJ
under licence from Savitri Books Ltd.

ISBN 1 85471 002 8

Designed by Mrinalini Srivastava
Printed and bound in Great Britain by
BPCC Hazells Ltd
Member of BPCC Ltd

A YEAR IN THE MEADOW

Benjamin Perkins, a painter and a naturalist, and author of several nature books, spent a year observing and recording the astonishing abundance of animals and plants harboured by Lapwing Meadows, an enclave of unspoilt meadowland lying hidden on the Essex-Suffolk border, in a part of England normally associated with the huge corn fields of intensive farming. Like a modern-day Gilbert White, the artist shares with us his delight in the natural world and his concern for a vanishing countryside and its wild life.

The land on this small patch is a little natural reserve. There is an ancient bridleway, open meadowland, marshy ground, a small wood, and blackthorn thickets where badgers and foxes find the seclusion they need. Numerous species of birds also find sanctuary on Lapwing Meadows. The variety of habitats explains the profusion and diversity of wildflowers and plants which has been captured by the artist in a series of exquisite flower paintings and of lively sketches of birds and other small animals. As the seasons unfold we are drawn into the ancient rhythms of the natural world, where the shifts in colour and light are matched by the changes in plant and animal activity, each an example of the delicate and mutually harmonious cooperation of nature and wild life when left to flourish alone.

This book of special days is a celebration of nature and of the special place it holds in our lives.

Ben Perkins '85.

January

1

2

3

4

5

6

The ancient trackway that runs along the meadows, blanketed in snow.

7
8
9
10
11
12

13

14

15

16

17

18

Wren.

| 19 |
| 20 |
| 21 |
| 22 |
| 23 |
| 24 |

A twig of pedunculate oak with hard,
round marble galls and artichoke or
hop galls on some of the buds.

25

26

27

28

29

30

31

A red fox in the wood.

A treecreeper searching for insects among crevices in the bark of a dead tree.

February

	1
	2
	3
	4
	5
	6

7

8

9

10

11

12

Old black poplar.

*February*_____

13

14

15

16

17

18

The first clumps of snowdrops.

*February*_____

19	
20	
21	
22	
23	
24	

25

26

27

28

29

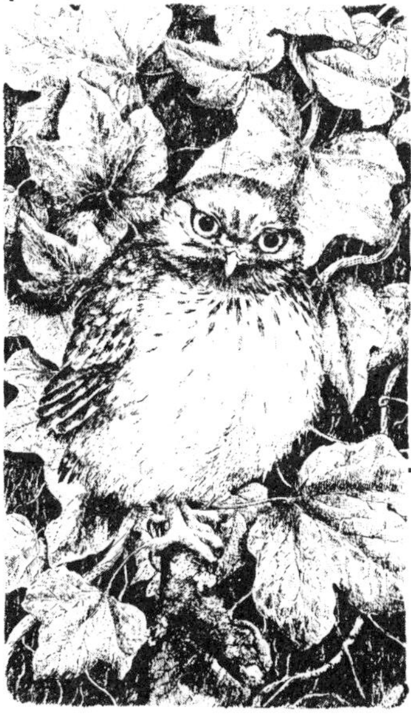

Juvenile little owl.

March

1

2

3

4

5

6

The first pale, lemon-yellow primroses begin to brighten the hedgerows and banks around the meadow.

March _____

7
8
9
10
11
12

	13
	14
	15

Black-headed gulls with one common gull.

March _____

16

17

18

19

20

21

22

23

Coltsfoot starting to flower and an early honey bee.

March _____

24	
25	
26	
27	
28	
29	

	30
	31

Green sandpiper.

April

1
2
3
4
5

Ground ivy and sweet vernal grass with a green-veined white butterfly and, on a leaf of ground ivy, the shieldbug Eysarcoris fabricii.

Badger near to the entrance to its set.

6

7

8

9

10

11

Red dead-nettle and a white form of the sweet violet add touches of colour to the hedgerows.

	12
	13
	14

Germander speedwell.

15

16

Kingfisher.

Reed bunting.

	17
	18
	19

April

Benjamin Perkins 1984.

	20
	21
	22
	23

Opposite: An early peacock butterfly with wings expanded basks in the spring sunshine among cowslip, daisy and field woodrush (left) and the purple flowers of ground ivy.
Below: Male three-spined stickleback.

Wood pigeon.

24

25

26

27

28

29
30

The ponies grazing on one of the meadows.

Cuckoo pint also known as
lords-and-ladies or jack-in-
the-pulpit.

Right: Three species of
violet. The bones of small
animals, such as this rabbit
skull, are frequently seen in
the woods at this time
of the year.

May

1

2

May_____

3

4

5

6

7

8

9

10

11

Rabbit stretching.

May

12

13

14

15

16

Hound's-tongue with its characteristic velvety leaves.

_May_____

17

18

19

Owl.

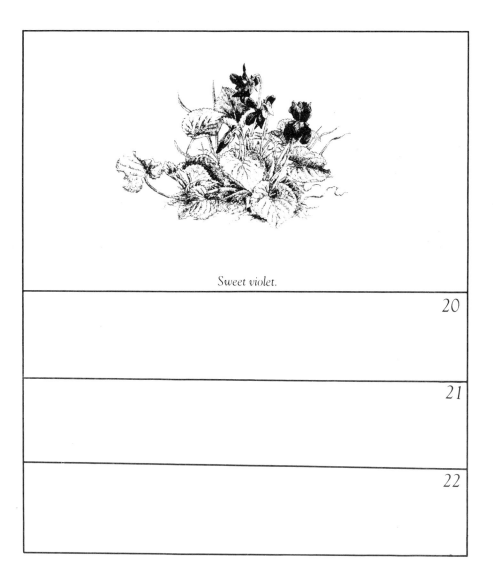

Sweet violet.

20

21

22

May

The large yellow flowers of the dandelion make a brave show and might be more admired if they were less familiar or less unpopular with gardeners.

_____

*Painted lady
butterfly on a
water mint flower.*

May

	23
	24
	25
	26

27

28

29

30

31

Pair of goldcrests.

June

1

Pair of lapwing.

2

3

June

4

5

6

7

8

_Meadow buttercup grows in profusion all over the meadows. The pale mauve cuckoo
flower, also known as lady's smock or milkmaids, is confined to the wetter parts._

June _____

9
10
11
12
13
14

15

16

Hen harrier.

17

18

19

20

21

The massed pink and white flowers of dog rose make a glorious show in the hedgerows and thickets.

*June*_____

22

23

24

25

26

27

	28
	29
	30

Southern hawker dragonfly.

July

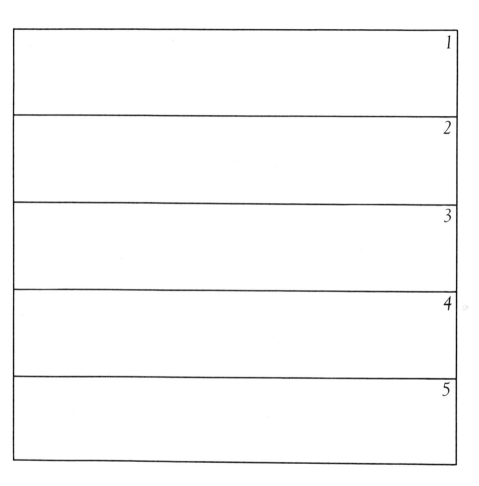

1

2

3

4

5

Hop trefoil on the left, the bright-yellow flowers of black medick mixed with red and white clover, are all plants of the open meadowland. The butterfly is a male orange-tip.

July _____

6	
7	
8	
9	
10	
11	

12

13

Grass snake running into the brook.

14

15

16

17

18

Hunting stoat.

Common spotted orchid on the left
with the rarer southern marsh orchid.

*July*_____

19	
20	
21	
22	
23	
24	

Long-tailed tits.

25

Below: Ragged robin. Opposite: The two most characteristic plants of the brook that runs through the meadows are water cress (in the foreground) and brooklime. The dragonfly is a male broad-bodied chaser.

A hunting pipistrelle bat.

26

27

28

29

30

31

August

1

2

A large white butterfly on tufted vetch. This plant climbs by means of tendrils among the tall surrounding vegetation of the meadows.

*August*_____

3

4

5

6

7

8

9

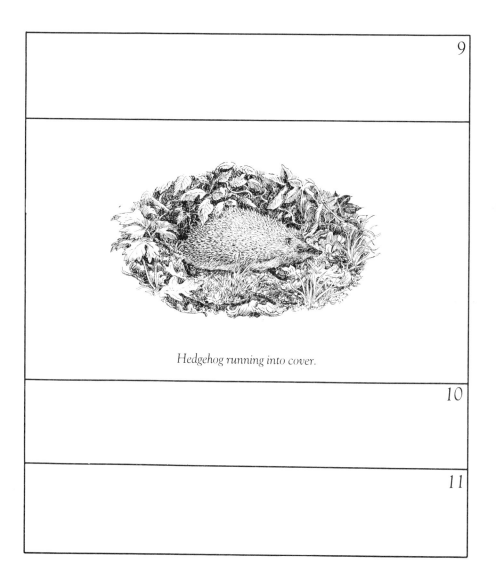

Hedgehog running into cover.

10

11

12
13

The purple flowers of self-heal are found all over the meadows. The butterfly is a meadow brown.

14

15

The lovely blue-flowered spikes of bugle favour damp and shady spots and are often hidden by taller plants.

16

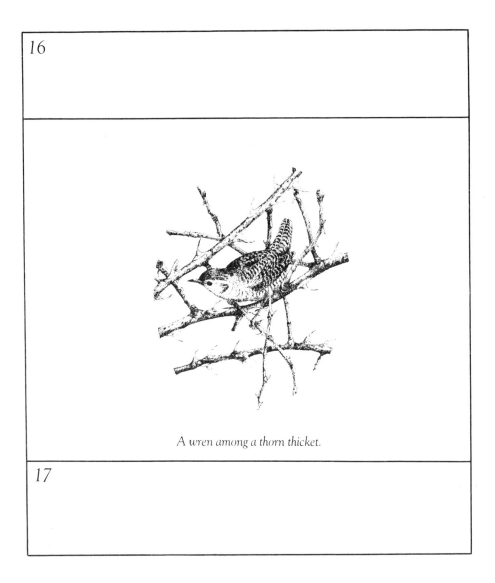

A wren among a thorn thicket.

17

18

19

20

21

22

23

August

24
25

Male and female speckled bush-crickets on bramble leaves.

Right: The flowers of high summer.

26

27

28

29

30

31

The stone bridge over the river.

September

1

2

3

Red admiral butterfly sunning itself against a screen of old man's beard and bramble.

4

5

6

7

The fruit of the sycamore tree.

8

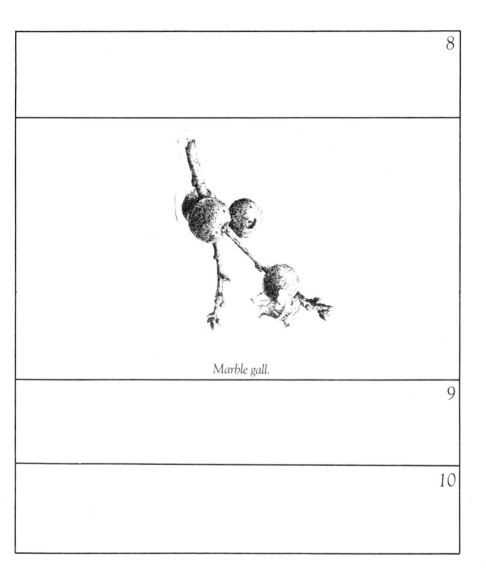

Marble gall.

9

10

September

11	
12	

Field mushrooms are very common on one of the meadows. The fallen leaves of crack willow show off their lovely autumn colouring.

Female dark bush-cricket.

	13
	14

September _____

15

16

17

18

19

20

Great spotted woodpecker.

| | 21 |

| | 22 |

| | 23 |

| | 24 |

Some of the late summer to autumn plants that are prominent on the meadows. From left to right: hardheads, agrimony, false fox sedge, devil's bit scabious, bristly ox-tongue, water figwort and great bindweed. The moth is a silver Y.

25

26

27

28

29

30

The cottage on the edge of the meadow.

October

1

2

3

4

5

Shaggy parasol mushrooms growing under a hawthorn bush.

October_____

6

7

8

The spiky husks of the sweet chestnut fruit.

9

Grey squirrel.

10

11

12

13

14

15

16

The shiny, black fruits of purging buckthorn which, as its name implies,
was formerly used as a purgative.

Crack willow.

	17
	18
	19
	20
	21
	22

23

24

Below: The mushroom Agaricus vaporius *with fallen horse chestnut fruits and a* colony of eyelash fungus. Right: *Hip of three different species of wild rose – dog rose, downy rose and field rose.*

October _____

25

26

27

28

29

30

31

Ancient black poplar.

The lustrous scarlet fruits of
black bryony glow jewel-like
in the hedgerows.

November

	1
	2
	3
	4
	5
	6

November _____

7

8

9

10

11

12

	13
	14
	15
	16

Fieldfares arriving.

The colourful fruits and leaves of the spindle tree.

17

18

19

20

21

22

*November*_____

23	
24	
25	
26	
27	
28	

29

30

A pair of snipe flying over the brook.

The brilliant-red berries and the shiny
leaves of the holly bush.

December

	1
	2
	3
	4

December _____

5
6
7
8
9
10

11

12

Pair of mallard under the rain.

*December*_____

13

14

15

16

17

18